The Estes
formula
for Breeding
Stakes Winners

Joseph A. Estes

The Russell Meerdink Co., Ltd.
1555 South Park Avenue
Neenah, Wisconsin 54956 USA
(920) 725-0955 Worldwide
Printed in the United States of America

Library of Congress-Cataloging-in-Publication Data

Estes, Joseph A. (Joseph Alvie), 1903-1970
    The Estes formula for breeding stakes winners / by
Joseph A. Estes.
    Includes index.
    ISBN 0-929346-62-9
    1. Race horses--Breeding.   I. Title.
SF338.E88 1998   98-44322
636.1'2082--ddc21   CIP

Published by:

The Russell Meerdink Company, Ltd.
1555 South Park Avenue
Neenah, WI 54956 USA
(920) 725-0955

Printed in the United States of America

Table *of* Contents

Preface 5

Chapter 1   Game of Many Notions 15

Chapter 2   The Best Blood .23

Chapter 3   The Opportunity 31

Chapter 4   Select for Merit, not Pedigree 35

Chapter 5   Producing Class = Racing Class 41

Chapter 6   The Average Earnings Index (AEI) 45

Chapter 7   The Four Plus Horse 49

Chapter 8   Increasing the Odds
                of Breeding a Stake's Winner 59

Chapter 9   Rating Sires 65

Chapter 10   Miscellaneous Thoughts on Breeding 71

Chapter 11   The Blood-Horse Compendium 77

Appendix I   Thoroughbred Season Earnings 87

Appendix II   Standardbred Season Earnings 89

Index 93

Joseph Alvie Estes

PREFACE

Tucked away on the second floor of the Keeneland Racecourse in Lexington, Kentucky is the Keeneland Association Library. The Library collects rare and valuable manuscripts on the lineage, breeding, history and tradition of the Thoroughbred. Some items in its collection are priceless.

The Library is open to the public. A visitor instinctively understands that this is a place that does not give ground easily to ideas and ways which have not stood the test of time. The decor of rich paneling, polished hardwood cases, stuffed furniture and Oriental carpets suggest the tradition, pageantry and quality of the Thoroughbred itself. It is a special place for anyone fascinated with racehorses.

It was here in the Library, in the fall of 1989, that I first learned of Joseph Alvie Estes.

On previous visits to the Library, I became acquainted with Miss Doris Jean Warren, its middle-aged, head librarian. Like the Library itself, Miss Warren did not capitulate to modern social convention. She was quick to point out that she was a Miss, not a Ms. She imposed a sense of formality to the place and all visitors fell under her watchful eye. Miss Warren had knowledge of each volume and paper in her collection far beyond that suggested in the Library's modest card catalog. It was always necessary to enlist her help to carry out any serious research. My frequent visits to the Library must have qualified my interest in the Thoroughbred as genuine, not just a passing fancy. On this particular day, Miss Warren invited me to explore the uncataloged boxes of papers and other materials neatly stacked in the Library's storage room. It was in one of these boxes that I found the first of Mr. Estes' papers describing his search for a formula to apply modern genetic principles to the breeding of Thoroughbreds.

Joe Estes (1903-1970) has been described by those to knew him as a poet, turf writer, statistician, computer programmer, geneticist, philosopher, bloodstock breeding expert and a man of "towering intellectual strength." Born in Graves County, Kentucky, he worked his way through the University of Kentucky serving as a sports editor of the *Lexington Leader* and later as sports editor and then city editor of the *Lexington Herald*. He graduated from the University of Kentucky in 1927 and began post graduate work at Columbia University in New York. It was during this time that he also served as the editor of *The Daily Running Horse* and later as the turf editor of the *Morning Telegraph*.

In 1930, Estes returned to Lexington to take the job of associate editor of *The Blood-Horse* and in 1935 became the magazine's editor, a post he held for 28 years. After leaving *The Blood-Horse*, Estes was named senior advisory editor of the *Thoroughbred Record*, title he held until his death.

In 1963, at Estes' urging, the Jockey Club established its Statistical Bureau. The role of the

Bureau was to computerize the breeding and racing records of all Thoroughbreds. Estes drew up the plans for the operation of the Statistical Bureau and was the Bureau's director of research. In 1969 he resigned that job to become the racing and breeding advisor to Nelson Bunker Hunt, the wealthy Texas oil man.

The Jay Lush Connection

Above all else, Estes was a student and an intellectual. He viewed the breeding of Thoroughbreds as an intellectual exercise and set out to devise a system which could predict the racing capacity of a racehorse within a reasonable

Jay Lush (1896-1982)

margin of error. Over the centuries, others have attempted to create similar systems with little success. None of the previous attempts at creating a system for breeding racehorses were based on genetic principles. Estes, the intellectual, began to study genetics.

About the same time that Estes took over control of *The Blood-Horse*, Jay Lush, a professor at Iowa State University, burst onto the scene as the architect of improving the quality of livestock through the use of genetic principles. In 1937, Lush published his book, *Animal Breeding Plans*, which to this day remains the definitive work on the subject of the genetic improvement of livestock. To many, Lush was the father of quantitative genetics.

The classical genetic study of peas conducted by Mendel forms the basis for modern genetics. Mendel learned how to manipulate the height of peas. The height of peas (phenotype) is under the control of a single or very few genes with little or no environmental impact to obscure the genes' effect. This type of trait is termed a *qualitative* trait. In contrast to this, many economically important traits in livestock are the result of many genes blending together to form the desirable (or undesirable) trait. Such a trait is termed a *quantitative* trait. Egg and milk production are examples of quantitative traits. There are many traits which a successful racehorse must exhibit. A stakes winning horse must be sound, have an efficient stride, exhibit "heart," have the capacity to breathe efficiently at racing speeds, etc.

A successful racehorse is the product of many genes which have blended together to create the desirable quantitative traits.

A hen which lays 300 eggs a year exhibits quantitative traits which are superior to a hen which lays only 200 eggs during the same period. A cow, which produces 20,000 pounds of milk, exhibits quantitative traits, which are superior to a cow which produces only 15,000 pounds. And a racehorse, which wins the Kentucky Derby or the Hambletonian and other important races, exhibits quantitative traits superior to those horses that do not accomplish such feats. The problem for the breeders of all these animals is identical: how does one transmit these desirable quantitative traits from this generation to the next? It is not difficult to understand why Estes turned to the research and writings of Lush to understand the problems of breeding Thoroughbreds.

According to Lush, the best guide to the probable performance of offspring is the known performance of both parents. By that standard, a stakes winning sire mated to a stakes winning mare is more likely to produce stakes winning offspring than if only one or neither of the parents is a stakes winner. This arrangement seems to follow the age-old advice of horsemen - breed best to best. When the performance (quantitative traits) of both parents is known, there is little to be gained by considering the performance of remote relatives. In other words, pedigree doesn't matter.

Estes adapted modern principles of livestock breeding to that of breeding racehorses. A key principle of livestock breeding is that the best gauge for predicting the performance of an animal's progeny is to look at the performance of the parents. The pedigree of an animal beyond its parents contributes little to predicting its own worth. Chart 1 dramatically makes the point.

Chart 1 is the one generally used by geneticists to predict progeny performance. To use Chart 1, the first step is to determine the degree to which the desired trait (i.e. egg laying capacity, running or trotting speed, etc.) is inherited. Chart 2 gives a summary of various studies on the heritabilty of racing capacity in both Thoroughbred and Harness horses. This chart is based on various studies which have shown racing capacity to be 20-50% inheritable. This means that 20-50% of a horse's racing capacity is based on the genes it inherits and 50-80% is influenced by environmental considerations such a training, conditioning and skill of its jockey or driver. If two horses are raised and trained under identical environmental conditions, the genetically superior animal should display superior racing capacity.

For the sake of this discussion, let us assume that the heritability of racing capacity is 25% and that you are considering breeding your mare, Pretty Girl. What will be the inherent, genetic racing capacity of Pretty Girl's foal?

The first step is to determine Pretty Girl's own racing capacity from her OWN record. By consulting Chart 1, you will see that the probability of predicting her genetic value using only Pretty Girl's own racing record is 50%. In other words, there is a 50% chance that her foal will inherit Pretty Girl's own racing capacity and a 50% chance that it will be something more or less than her own racing capacity. The predictability using Pretty Girl's own racing records and those of both her parents, the probability rises only 7% to 57%. But if Pretty Girl has no racing record, and the only records available are those of both her parents, the probability of accurate prediction falls to 35%.

What is important is the genetic value of the two animals to be mated. The records of distant relatives matter little.

If breeding good laying hens, good producing cows or fast racehorses is nothing more than "breeding best to best," then the only problem

Chart 1 Accuracy of predicting genetic value from own and ancestor records (percent)			
	Heritability		
Records Used	10%	25%	50%
Own	32%	50%	71%
Own + 1 parent or progeny	35	53	73
Only 1 parent or progeny	16	25	35
Own + 2 parents	38	57	76
Only 2 parents	23	35	50
Own + 1 grandparent	32	51	71
Only 1 grandparent	8	12	18
Own + 4 grandparents	35	53	73
Only 4 grandparents	16	25	35

Chart 2
Likely ranges for heritability for some traits

Trait	Heritability
Thoroughbred races	
Time	20-35%
Handicap-performance rate	30-50%
Trotting and pacing races	
Time	20-35%
Earnings	20-35%

Charts 1 and 2 reprinted from The Horse by J. Warren Evans, Anthony Borton, Harold Hintz and L. Dale Van Vleck, 1990, W.H. Freeman and Company pps. 560-61

remaining is how to define what constitutes "best." One of the most basic steps in breeding improved livestock is to define an ideal or standard against which all animals may be judged. This usually results in the creation of an index against which the quantitative traits of a sire, dam and progeny may be measured. To develop a breeding plan for Thoroughbreds, Estes first needed to establish an index by which he could evaluate racing performance. He accomplished this through the creation of the Average Earnings Index, which is discussed in detail in Chapter 6. The Average Earnings Index for Thoroughbreds is readily available in breeding publications and from the Jockey Club and continues to be used as a yardstick for measuring racing performance. Few Thoroughbred breeders, however, are aware of why it was developed in the first place and even fewer use it in their breeding program.

The genetic principles Estes set forth for breeding Thoroughbreds is equally applicable for breeding Standardbreds. Unfortunately, there is no readily available Average Earnings Index for Standardbreds but the breeder can easily devise his own index as described elsewhere in this book.

During his years as editor of *The Blood-Horse*, Estes wrote frequently about the Average Earnings Index and how breeders could use it. As time went on, his philosophies and theories came into focus. Unfortunately, however, one needed to be a regular reader of *The Blood-Horse* and Estes fan to follow his ideas from article-to-article. Nowhere on the pages of *The Blood-Horse*, that we can find, did Estes include an entire summary of his formula for breeding stakes winners.

That brings us back to Miss Doris Jean Warren, the Keeneland librarian. A dedicated librarian rarely throws anything away, believing that there is someone in search of each document that has been archived. Among the many papers Miss Warren guarded over the years were copies of several educational talks which Estes made to groups of breeders. Here in the Keeneland Library was the Estes formula for breeding stakes winners. It is these papers that form the basis of this book. Thank you Miss Warren.

Chapters 1 through 3 are from a speech which Estes gave to the Thoroughbred Club of America on March 3, 1934. This was the time which Estes was just beginning his research. Chapters 4 through 10 are from the *Stud Managers Handbook*, a book based on lectures presented at the Stud Managers Courses held at the University of Kentucky from 1951-1954, and a talk given at the Thoroughbred Club of America testimonial dinner on October 18, 1962.

Other than minor editing, these are Estes' words.

In Chapter 11, we have included excerpts from articles which appeared in *The Blood-Horse* throughout the years.

Russell Meerdink
Neenah, Wisconsin
September, 1998

Chapter 1

A Game of
Many Notions

My addressing the Thoroughbred Club of America on the subject of breeding horses is not greatly different from the old maid's lecturing parents on how to raise children. What little I know about Thoroughbreds is mostly out of the books and the papers; what you know of them is mostly out of the stables and the paddocks and from the race tracks. What you have learned is infinitely more valuable than what I have learned, and I would a thousand times rather you would tell me what you know than to try to tell you what I think I know. I feel like a peddler come to sell pretzels at a banquet. I say pretzels advisedly, for I am sure that most of you will take what I have to say with a grain of salt.

Breeding Thoroughbreds is a game of many notions, many theories and much confusion. There are, in fact, so many theories and so many things which tend to prove and to disprove each of them that the average breeder will frequently tell you "they're all well enough bred," and leave you with the impression that the main requirement for being a successful breeder is the faculty of being lucky. What I want to do today is to discuss the question whether there is anything in any of these theories which can be depended on, whether there is any grain in the chaff, whether there are any generalizations which will stand up in the face of all facts, whether, in short, there is any horse sense in all the horseradish.

Before I go into that problem I want to remind you of something you know, but something you are always forgetting, namely, percentage. Percentage is what makes race tracks possible, as it is applied to the betting end of the sport. It is just as important in breeding. If you take a pair of dice, shake them and throw them down, no man can say with certainty what the total number of spots will be on the first throw, or on the second, or third, or on any one cast. but if you throw a pair of dice a million times, any man can say with certainty that the number seven will show more often than any others, and he can establish with virtual certainty the limits within which each of the other possible totals will occur. The same thing applies to breeding horses. Don't make your generalizations from one horse, in as much as you are able to know the record of all horses and matings. I give you this little song-and-dance by way of explanation that whatever generalizations you hear from me today will be based on percentage and will be based on all horses I know anything about - and if anyone has objection to anything I say, I hope he bases it on more than one horse, because one horse won't upset this apple cart.

Theories in the Discard

First, let's take a few theories for a slight preliminary examination. There are so many of them that clutter up our path that we have to kick a few of them aside before we can find standing room. There is, for instance, the notion that racing ability is

Sweep

inherited along with coat-color, that a Fair Play isn't of much account unless he inherited his sire's chestnut coat color. I suppose, by the same token, that it is the same phenomenon which made good sires of *Sir Gallahad III, Black Toney, Sweep, Ben Brush, etc., for they always transmitted a coat color which approximated their own.

There is also the theory, generally known to horsemen as the saturation theory, and mentioned among biologists under the name of telegony, which says that if you breed a mare repeatedly to the same stallion, she will thereafter have foals which bear the characteristics of that stallion, even if the foals are by some other horse. I have heard that sermon preached repeatedly, by some of the most successful breeders in the country. There is a large group of horsemen who feel that the sire plays the leading part in determining the characteristics of the foal, and there is the opposite-minded group who believe the dam is the more important. Neither of these

17

theories makes much sense. I think the most sensible statement I ever heard in this connection was made by Del Holeman: "If you have a good sire he's 50 per cent of your stud; if you have a bad sire, he's 100 per cent of your stud."

There is another theory, originated, I believe, by the editor of *Horse and Hound* in London, who is one of the best informed and most interesting Turf writers I have ever read. His notion is that the sire and dam, for the best results, should be of nearly the same age, and proves his case with a long string of examples of good horses. It means nothing to him that good horses and bad horse are bred by this method and that the curve of age incidence among the bad ones is exactly the same as among the good ones. These and other notions of the same ilk are widely believed among horsemen, who might as well believe in ghosts and goblins. I don't know much about the theories I have just mentioned, for the same reason that I don't know much about voodooism. I don't see the use of making extensive investigations of propositions unless there is some evidence of truth. And I can tell you without the slightest hesitancy that there is no support for any of these theories.

Chromosomes

I suppose that since the beginning of his intelligence man has realized some of the phenomena of heredity but it is only in the last, three-quarters of a century that much progress has been made in determining the mechanism of heredity. I wish I had the time and the technical knowledge to detail here a few of the extremely -

almost unbelievably - complex series of events which take place at the very beginning of the embryonic life of a foal, or of any living thing, for that matter. I haven't the time or the knowledge, but I don't see how I can get very far without saying a word or so about chromosomes.

Chromosomes are little thread-like things, of different shapes and sizes, that a microscope will show all rolled up together inside the reproductive cells of animals, in the ovum of the mare or the wiggling sperm cell of the stallion. When the sperm cell enters the egg produced by the mare those chromosomes begin a most remarkable series of maneuvers, in which the female's chromosomes are paired off against the male's. I suppose a man looking through a microscope would be reminded of an old country dance, in which you "Grab yer partner by the craw and swing her all around old Arkansaw." But when the dance is over, the chromosomes of the male and the female have formed a coalition, have "married," if you please, and have started keeping house for themselves. The coalition they have formed represents the foal that is to be born eleven months later. The character of that foal, as far as heredity will affect it, is probably settled.

Now, the point I want to make is this. Each one of those chromosomes on each side of the house, from the mare and from the sire, represents a definite part of the character of the foal-to-be. The chromosomes, or rather, the genes, which represent color will get together and determine the color of the foal. Other combinations will determine the skeleton, still others the temperament, etc., etc. We

19

don't know how this is done, but we do know that the horse has 32 chromosomes, and each chromosome appears to hold several factors determining different characters. Suppose you take 32 dice and throw them down over here, and 32 more dice and throw them down over there; perhaps you can imagine the enormous number of possibilities you would have. They would be uncountable. Well, the same thing applies to the mating of two horses. The possibilities as to the offspring are limitless. And you can no more go down inside the fertilized egg cell and influence the chromosomes one way or the other than you could lead a camel through the eye of a needle, if you'll pardon me for borrowing a figure of speech from the pulpit.

What can you do, then, in order to get a happy combination of chromosomes and consequently a good race horse? The only thing you can do is to breed from the best individuals and from the best bloodlines possible all the time. This means nothing except that the chromosomes from the best horses will carry a larger percentage of desirable characteristics than the chromosomes from bad horses. Getting back to the dice again, you are simply giving yourself a mathematical chance to throw more naturals. You are using loaded dice. It's percentage again. I guarantee you that Man o'War can sire horses as bad as Cork Elm if only the chromosomes get together in the worst possible arrangement. Some of you will probably recall the persistence of James W. Cromwell in breeding Clark Chief to Lute Boyd in an effort to get the proper combination of their qualities in Harrison Chief, one of the foundations of saddle and show horse.

The Inheritance of Color

Some characteristics are inherited as blends. Take, for instance, height. If you mate a stallion 15 hands tall with a mare 17 hands tall, you would expect the offspring to be about 16 hands tall. If you mate a six-furlong sprinter with a Belmont Stakes winner, you would expect a horse whose best distance would be somewhere in between.

There are other characteristics which are inherited by what are known as Mendel's laws. For these characteristics there is no blending. It is one or the other. In color, for instance, the mating of a bay with a chestnut doesn't produce a foal whose color is a blend of bay and chestnut. It is either bay or chestnut or rather, it is either chestnut or not chestnut, for it may be darker than bay. Horses inherit their colors according to definite laws of hereditary.

The chart I have here will give an example of inheritance of color. The symbol at the top left represents a pure dominant bay horse, and, because he is known to all of you, I have put down the name of *Sir Gallahad III as a concrete example. At the top right is a symbol representing a chestnut mare (Marguerite). A chestnut horse can transmit no color factor except chestnut, and a pure dominant bay (or brown) will have no dominant offspring. The foal resulting from the mating was necessarily bay, that is non-chestnut. Bay is the outward color of Gallant Fox, but as for his hereditary make-up, that is not all the story. He carries in his germ cells both the dominant bay and the recessive chestnut factors. The chart shows further what will happen with regard to the color of Gallant Fox's offspring. From his matings with chestnut mares he will get 50 per cent bays and 50 per cent chestnuts. (Whenever the bay factor is present it is dominant, and the foal can not be chestnut.) From his matings with impure dominant bay mares he will sire 75 per cent bays and 25 per cent chestnuts and one-third of the bays will be pure dominants. These ratios are brought about in strict keeping with the percentage of probability. It is simply the story of the dice once more.

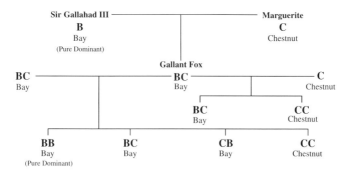

And if color, which we can see and identify instantaneously, is inherited in strict accordance with laws, we have some right, I think, to assume that other characteristics, not quite so recognizable, are inherited in strict accordance with rules. What confuses us is the fact that characteristics are inherited separately, and not in bundles (with a few exceptions), and any horse to be a good racer, must have a large number of good characteristics.

Chapter 2

The Best Blood

But I have talked too long on chromosomes. What are the facts that the average race horse breeder, at his home out in the country, miles away from a microscope or a textbook, needs to know about breeding horses? Well, there are several.

First, he ought to know that in every generation of horses there are a few outstanding individuals which dominate all the rest, as far as breeding is concerned. I have here a chart which indicates what I mean. The names on this chart indicate, for England and for America, the horses which have assumed the leading roles as material for the pedigrees of the best racers. These are not all the important horses of the last 200 years, of course, but here on this page you see the names of less than three dozen horses which have had more to do with making the Thoroughbred what he is today than did thousands of their contemporaries.

Now, what made these horses stand out from their fellows? Nothing more nor less than the fact that their chromosomes carried a high percentage of favorable characteristics. *These horses were loaded dice.* There was simply a better percentage in your favor if you had sons or daughters or descendants of these horses.

As one generation succeeded another, it was found that these outstanding horses were indispensable in pedigrees, that is, in the production

About	English	American
1718	Godolphin Arabian Partner	
1760	Herod Eclipse Highflyer	*Diomed Sir Archy
1830	Birdcatcher Touchstone Pochahontas Voltaire Melbourne	*Glencoe
1850	Stockwell Newminster	Lexington *Bonnie Scotland *Australian
1880	St. Simon Galopin Isonomy Hampton Hermit Bend Or	Domino Ben Brush Hindoo Hanover
1900	Cyllene	Fair Play

of good horses. And you can expect certain horses within a few miles of us today to be indispensable in breeding the good horses of tomorrow.

It is not possible to predict in advance the occurrence of these key horses. Their being born depends to a large extent upon an accidental arrangement of chromosomes - not accidental in fact, but for all practical purposes accidental. Neither Fair Play nor Mahubah figured to produce a Man o'War, neither *Sir Gallahad III nor Marguerite figured to breed a Gallant Fox, neither St. Germans nor Bonus could have been predicted as the parent of a Twenty Grand. Breeding a horse of such high class may be compared with throwing seven with the dice for, say, 12 times in succession. It can happen, but it can't happen very often.

The Best Blood, By Statistics

As I say, you can't predict the occurrence of great horses - the key horses, I mean, of breeding development, such as St. Simon, Bend Or, Isonomy, Domino, etc. But what you can do is to identify them as quickly as possible after they do appear. We have various sets of statistics to guide us in the selection of these stars of the pedigree firmament. We have lists of leading sires, leading broodmare sires, leading 2-year-old sires, family tables, and various other guides. But none of these is especially valuable in giving statistical information on the strength of bloodlines. They concentrate attention to some extent on male lines, to some extent on female lines, and to some extent on individual horses, but all the middle portion of the pedigree is neglected. that is a mistake, and it is a mistake that is being made every day.

Horsemen almost invariably attach more importance to the top line and to the bottom line of the pedigree than to any of the bloodstrains in between. Why is that? Well, as nearly as I can figure it out, the reason lies in the fact that it is impossible for the average person to remember all the names in the middle of a pedigree, but it is no trick for him to follow back two lines, the top and the bottom, and keep them rather clearly in his mind. But the

25

characteristics of the foal are just as likely to come from this middle ground as from anywhere else in the pedigree.

There is another thing of which the breeder can be sure, and that is that the best individuals will produce the best in a dependable majority of cases. The pedigrees of the best race horses are made up of names of the best race horses. And don't let the exceptions to that rule confuse you to the extent that you believe the rule will not work.

In my book performance is more important than pedigree as an indication of the probable failure or success of an individual as a breeder. Breeding race horses is a continuous process of picking the best individuals for reproduction. If for ten successive years we were to destroy our best individuals for reproduction. If for ten successive years we were to destroy our best individuals and use their inferior full brothers and sisters for breeding purposes, we would set the race of Thoroughbreds back so far that it would take us fifty years to repair the damage we had done. In only an occasional instance will a horse transmit qualities which he himself did not have, and if a sire had no speed of his own, you needn't breed your mare to that sire and expect to reproduce the speed that one of his grandparents had.

The Problem of Inbreeding

Now I want to say a word about inbreeding, a subject about which there are many notions and many confusions. The first principle of inbreeding is that it fixes characteristics. With the aid of inbreeding, man can mold domestic animals to suit his own will. He can inbreed cattle to get large milk

26

production, or rich milk production (not both at once), or he can breed for beef, or for the show ring. With hogs, he can develop the lard type, or the bacon type, or the ham type, or whatever happens to be his fancy. The saddle horse was developed here within a few miles of Lexington in the last three-quarters of a century by means of continuous inbreeding to desirable types of horses. Even in human beings inbreeding has been used to fix types and I point you for, example, to the chosen people of God. As a race they have cut through every stratum of civilization and kept their own clear-cut characteristics, like a rich lode of gold running through the earth.

I want to show you an example of type fixing by means of inbreeding. Here is a pedigree of Comet, granddaddy of all the Shorthorns. Comet is not only the Eclipse of the Shorthorn breed, he is the Eclipse, the Herod and the Matchem all rolled into one.

$$
\text{COMET} \left\{ \begin{array}{l} \text{Favorite} \quad \left\{ \begin{array}{l} \text{Bolingbroke} \\ \text{Phoenix} \end{array} \right. \\ \text{Young Phoenix} \quad \left\{ \begin{array}{l} \text{Favorite} \\ \text{Phoenix} \end{array} \right. \end{array} \right.
$$

The same sort of persistent inbreeding, though never as intensive as in this Shorthorn pedigree, was used to fix the type of the Thoroughbred, but the race was fortunate in that it had more than one individual to use as the basis for inbreeding. In every generation of the Thoroughbred we have had a fair assortment of comparatively unrelated individuals to pick from. That is why there is no particular merit in inbreeding today; though, at the same time, there is no particular harm in it.

Are there any adverse effects from inbreeding? You understand, of course, that it will emphasize the good qualities and the bad qualities of the ancestor whose blood is intensified. But I mean, are there any ill effects from inbreeding itself, apart from the individual concerned? You can make this generalization and be safe: That inbreeding, practiced successively and intensively, will result in lowered vitality and fertility - unless it is accompanied by a most rigid selection of the basis of vitality and fertility. But horse breeders need not worry about that. They do not inbreed their animals that much. I would say, therefore, that inbreeding, in itself, will do absolutely no harm. Whether it does good will depend upon the individual which is the basis of inbreeding.

Hybrid Vigor

But the most important phenomenon of inbreeding, from the practical point of view - from the point of view that you can use it and profit by it - is this: That unrelated inbred strains, if brought together by mating, will produce an increased vitality. For instance, if you have a mare inbred to Hanover, send her to a horse inbred, say, to St. Simon. The resulting foal, in a large percentage of cases, will prove to have more vitality, more class, than either of the parents. This is no theory. It is a demonstrated fact, repeatedly demonstrated. The phenomenon is commonly known as hybrid vigor. It is, to a lesser degree, the same phenomenon that occurs when you breed your mare to a jack. Now, the mare has no ancestors which are kin to any of the ancestors of the jack (except by marriage, possibly).

28

The resulting foal is known as a mule, and every horseman here knows that the mule will have more size, more strength, will live longer, will have more sense, will do more work and will eat less corn than either of his parents. In the Thoroughbred field, there are many examples. One of the best known is Sarazen. I would call your attention at the same time to Wise Counsellor, a phenomenon of breeding - and the one horse which is usually pointed out to refute any man who tries to make an intelligent generalization about how to breed horses. No sooner it is out of his mouth than some one rises up and says, "What about Wise Counsellor?" Well, what about him? I don't know how he happened to happen, and you don't either. The thing to consider is that he did happen and he is here. And the important thing to consider is that he is inbred to *Leamington with four lines to that horses, three of them close up. Outside of the *Leamington and his Hanover male line, he has virtually no other lines which are fashionable today. With a horse bred that way you can put into practice the principle of hybrid vigor. If you breed a horse bred like that to mares inbred to St. Simon, Galopin, Bend Or and Isonomy, you'll have more stakes winners popping out than you can find box stalls for. That's not the whole story of hybrid vigor, but we have to quit somewhere.

Chapter 3

The Opportunity

By inbreeding and outcrossing and selection, we have standardized the Thoroughbred today for certain qualities. First and most important of these is speed. After this come other qualities - stamina, toughness (soundness, that is) and another quality which can hardly be described in one word. Some call it heart, some call it the head, some say temperament, some say disposition - but the important part of it is the WILL-TO-RUN, the WILL-To-WIN - and that is a heritable characteristic, just as surely as coat color is.

In America we have, I think, standardized our horses for another quality, and that is early maturity. In general, we have great two-year-olds, fair three-year-olds, and - find me some four-year-olds. This accentuation of early maturity - which can be bred into horses just as certainly as the sheepmen of the Blue Grass breed it into their lambs - has had a tremendous influence on the development of the other qualities of which I spoke. It has increased speed, almost to the last notch; the throttle is nearly wide open. It has diminished the more commendable and more desirable qualities of stamina and soundness.

In this respect, I think it is about time that American horsemen came to their senses. They have just about reached the crossroads now, and they may as well begin to make up their minds which way they are going, toward more speed or toward more stamina and more soundness. A few days ago I was talking to a scientist who has given most of his life to the study of animal breeding, and he said to me that the Thoroughbred and the Standardbred horses have just about reached the physical limit of their speed. I asked him what proof of that statement he had, and he gave me a little lecture on physics and pendulums and muscles, and would up with this story.

He said that after Lee Axworthy died, his bones were taken to the American Museum of Natural History in New York and there mounted as a part of the exhibition which also includes the statue of Sysonby as representative of the Thoroughbred. He said that the last time he was in New York he talked to the man who had assembled the skeleton of Lee Axworthy, and that the scientist pointed out to him a remarkable thing. In the knee joints, it could be seen where Lee Axworthy, in his racing days, had made such an effort to increase the length of his stride that he had actually worn out places in the rim of the socket by reaching so far that the hinge-joint had been made to encompass distances that nature had supposedly put beyond its limitations. The horse's will to win was so great that he had enlarged the physical powers of his own body. But naturally that process could not be continued long, nor could such a trait be passed on to his get.

So there is some of the evidence that we are near the limits of speed. And if you want more evidence, make a big red mark on your barn door every time you read of a fast horses breaking down - and see how long it takes to paint your barn.

It seems to me that the time has come when a man could make a commercial success of breeding for stamina and soundness and courage in connection with speed, rather than breeding for speed to the exclusion of these other qualities. Speed can be developed to such an extent that it may destroy its possessor. Breeding for early maturity - how many horses have you seen that reached the highest point of their development in the sales ring at Saratoga? - breeding for early maturity can root out a lot of other commendable qualities.

If American horsemen will only take it, they have an opportunity such as is possessed by the horsemen of no other country. In England there is virtually no great horse bred whose pedigree does not bear a strong concentration of the blood of St. Simon, Galopin, Bend Or, Isonomy, Hampton and Hermit, a majority of those six key horses. The other night I ran through the pedigrees of 105 outstanding horses of recent years, as set down in F. Mainwaring Sharp's book, and of the 105 I found that 32 were inbred with three free generations or less, and 11 of them were inbred primarily to St. Simon. I mention this as only as instance of how much England, the only great Thoroughbred exporting nation in the world, has come to depend on these bloodstrains. In America we have all those strains, and we also have other strong lines - Ben Brush, Domino, Hanover, Fair Play. From France we have brought over still other lines, though these are to some extent manufactured from the English cloth. The idea is that America, for horses as well as for people, is the melting pot of the world, and out of this melting pot we could produce an alloy stronger and better than

33

any of the original metals which went into the crucible. And, with the key horses of the whole world to pick from, we should develop a strain of horses which are superior to any in the world - and we would already have done so if we had spent less time breeding horses that can work a quarter in 22 seconds and more time in breeding horses that can run a mile and a half in 2:31.

Chapter 4

Select for Merit, not Pedigree

To begin my part of this discussion, I shall quote one sentence from *Animal Breeding Plans*, by Dr. Jay L. Lush, who is probably the leading authority on heredity in farm animals. He says:

"The general conclusion regarding pedigree selection is that it should usually be a minor accessory to individual selection, being permitted to sway the balance in making decisions which are fairly close on individual merit."

I shall attempt to show that this generalization applies the breeding of race horses.

In breeding Thoroughbreds, pedigrees do have their importance, of course. But that importance has been exaggerated, by every generation of breeders, far beyond its actuality. All the "systems" which have filled the literature of Thoroughbred breeding - Bruce Lowe, Vuillier, inbreeding, outcrossing, nicks, and all that - are based upon pedigrees, and hence are not only useless but costly, because they tend to keep in production mares and stallions which, under any realistic method of appraisal, would be taken off the expense account.

If pedigrees are relatively unimportant, is there a more satisfactory basis for the selection of breeding stock? There is. And this is the key to the good or ill fortune a breeder may expect; he must find, one way or another, by design or by accident, the individuals, male and female, with the genetic constitution to produce animals which meet his standard of excellence - whatever that standard may be.

Many breeders expect to find these individuals the easy way, by accident, by luck. Such is the chance nature of heredity that occasionally they do so. But the chances are so low that no breeder should expect to survive as such with no better plan of action than to wait for his luck to strike. I know of no extensive breeding operation which has been successful merely because it has been lucky.

Where, then, do we begin planning? With the selection of individuals for breeding stock. How do we select these individuals? Mostly according to their own performance and their own appearance - that is to say according to phenotype.

We should select breeding stock mainly on the basis of individual merit. We should cull on the basis of the merit of the progeny, for the progeny will indicate, as the pedigree can never do, the genetic make-up of the parent.

Once we have determined, from its own performance and from the performance of its progeny, the genetic make-up (or genotype) of an individual, there is virtually nothing more to be gained by exploration of that individual's ancestry. Once we have found, for instance, that *Pharamond II can transmit only the bay-brown color and cannot sire chestnuts, the pedigree has become useless insofar as color is concerned - it adds nothing to the knowledge we have. As a matter of fact, *Sickle, with the same pedigree, the same sire and dam, and with the same color as *Pharamond II, did transmit the chestnut color. Only the progeny, and not the pedigree, could reveal the difference.

Hurry On, to take one more example, was a chestnut and all his parents and grandparents were chestnuts. But there is no such thing as intensification of a characteristic. It is either there in the genetic make-up or it is not there, and when we have determined whether it is present or absent, it is pointless to search among the ancestors for further evidence. On the average, Hurry On will get exactly the same proportion of chestnut offspring as any other chestnut sire.

As with coat color, so with racing class. A high-class son of Man o'War has a good chance to become a success as a sire, if bred to good mares. A no-good son of Man o'War has, for all practical purposes, no more chance of success in the stud than a no-good son of a less distinguished sire.

The possession of racing class is the best preliminary evidence that an individual will be able to pass it on to the next generation. By preliminary evidence I mean, of course, the evidence available before the progeny can be appraised. This preliminary evidence is of the highest importance to the breeder, especially in the selection of broodmares, for if he waits to purchase mares whose progeny already have proved their capacity to produce good horses, he must buy, usually, at prices so high that the odds are against him, rather than in his favor.

The possession of racing class does not necessarily mean that the individual will pass it on. It only indicates the favorable odds. It means a higher probability of good progeny than if the racing class were not there, or rather, if it were lower degree.

Some breeders find it difficult to believe this. Even those who do believe it are likely to respond with an immediate "yes, but---." Yes, but, even if you do have an individual with racing class, you want the best pedigree you can get, don't you?

This is the crossroads for the breeder. Once he has accepted pedigree as an important criterion for the selection of breeding stock, to be used along with judgment according to the apparent or demonstrated merit of the individual, he has confused and slowed up his own progress. For if he assigns any importance to the pedigree, he is likely to assume that it has equal importance with, or possibly greater importance than, the individual itself. His standards will become so mixed that in many cases he will be selecting breeding stock simply because the pedigree looks good to him.

There is a correlation between one generation and the next, if racing class is accepted as the only standard for judging. This correlation is of course rather low, after the fashion of heredity patterns when the desirable animal is the extreme rather than the average. Despite the fact that the correlation based on racing class is low, it is the only correlation which has been demonstrated. It is something definite, measured repeatedly, dependable within fairly well known limits.

The fact of the matter is, of course, that we shall continue to take pedigree very seriously and use our judgment of it in selecting breeding stock. This despite the fact that we have no objective means of measuring the relative worth of pedigrees, and no likelihood that it would be accepted if we did have an objective means of measuring.

Even if a method of evaluating pedigrees were worked out and accepted by breeders, it is virtually certain that the correlation between the pedigree of one generation and the performance of the next would be considerably lower than the correlation between performance of one generation and the performance of the next.

Chapter 5

Producing Class = Racing Class

We do have a relationship between the racing class of one generation and that of the next. A relationship implies a statistical predictability. And the only science in this business, if breeding race horses is in the mathematics of probability - the degree to which we can estimate the future correctly. Until we know a great deal more about pedigree than we know now, I think we would do better to accept racing class, wherever it appears, as evidence of favorable breeding probability, without qualification on the basis of pedigree.

It seems worth the trouble to set forth some evidence in support of the contention that racing class in one generation is the best available evidence of the probability of racing class in the next. To many of you and possibly to most of you, this evidence will not be necessary; you will have studied the question long enough to have drawn the same conclusion. Nevertheless, the volume of Thoroughbred production in North America, the sales catalogues, and any sample representing the average of the breed, are enough to indicate how little trust our breeders, as a group, are willing to place upon such an objective standard. Hence we are perhaps justified in placing some witnesses on the stand to make our case.

With reference to males, there appears to be a rather general agreement that the best race horse in any group is the best sire prospect. There is always, of course, a disposition on the part of breeders to qualify their acceptance of a sire prospect on the basis of his pedigree, and at the moment it appears futile to argue against such qualification. It is possible that some breeders emphasize pedigree entirely too much for their own good, crying down a top-class young stallion because they consider his bloodlines unfashionable, and thus, by withholding their best mares from him, condemning him to mediocrity or actual failure.

Nevertheless, breeders are much more willing to accept racing class as an indicator of breeding probability in the sire than they are when it comes to the selection of broodmares. A contributor to the *Washington Horse* recently voiced this feeling very positively: "It is a thousand to one that a champion race mare will never reproduce her equal - and a hundred to one that she will not even produce a stake winner." Those are nice odds, if you could get them. We shall see how correct they are.

The hypothesis that racing class in the mare is the best indicator of producing class I have tested many times, with various samples. Always the same answer results. But when I was given the compliment of being asked to speak to this group of horsemen, whose wisdom has come from experience, it immediately occurred to me that I had better check once more before addressing such an audience.

It happened that some months ago, Mr. Clarkson Beard of Greentree Farm had brought to me his own list of the best ten colts and best ten fillies foaled in each of the ten years beginning with 1940. Of course I asked immediately for the privilege of copying the list, since things of this sort represent a considerable amount of work, and cannot be turned out easily or by anyone who does not have a considerable background for the task.

I attempted to supplement Mr. Beard's work by listing the best ten fillies foaled in each of the years beginning with 1930. These were needed in order to provide a fairly large sample of mares with a considerable production record. I could hardly expect complete agreement with the selections I have made. Usually, in any crop, it would be easy enough to reach an agreement on seven or eight and possibly nine; it is the last one, two, or three that would provoke the argument. Always the final decision as to the tenth of ten must be more or less arbitrary, and I shall be delighted if anyone wished to try improving the list as I have made it. Whatever substitutions are made, it is unlikely that they would effect any material change in the conclusions.

It would have been better, of course, if I had been able to take the best hundred mares of each ear, but such a task was quite impossible. I think most of you would join me in wishing that we had a year-end ranking, something like the Experimental Free handicap done be Mr. J.B. Campbell and *The Blood-Horse* Handicap done by Mr. F.E. Kilroe, which would be confined to fillies, assigning weights to the best in the different age groups. The handicaps we do have point out our best broodmare prospects. But if we had handicaps which were restricted to female runners, we would have a much larger list of the best prospects.

We need such reference lists for reasons which seem obvious. The best hundred race mares foaled in any given year will produce no more foals than will be sired by the three or four males of the same age. Sires are more quickly proven through their progeny. With mares it is highly important that we have an estimate of their breeding value in advance, since in many cases they will have finished more than half their careers as broodmares before we have a reasonable clue to their breeding potential. But that is, perhaps, daydreaming. Let us get back to our best ten.

Chapter 6

The Average Earnings Index (AEI)

Some of you are familiar with the average-earnings index which I devised a few years ago. Others are not. I shall attempt to explain it as briefly as possible.

You are all aware of the tremendous increase in purses in recent years, and you will have noticed that the list of leading money winners is made up, in the main, of horses which have raced within the last decade. Citation earned a million, Man o'War a quarter-million. The Porter, foaled in 1915, one of the best handicappers of his time, raced five seasons and earned less than $74,000. Greek Ship is retiring to the stud with earnings over $300,000. Man o'War was the first sire whose get earned more than $3,000,000 - a total which is now commonplace for a good sire. It is plain that the dollar, of itself, cannot provide a basis of comparison between horses which raced in different times.

But we need comparisons in order to devise at least a crude form of race horse genetics. So I attempted to create an index which would correspond roughly to the batting and fielding averages of baseball, and to various other statistics where accomplishment is measured in ratio to opportunity. The result is crude, but it is more dependable than previous data, more adaptable as a basis for prediction.

In 1940 the total money distributed in stakes and purses in North America was just under $16 million. In each year since 1949 the annual total has been above $50 million. There has been, of course, an increase in the number of runners, from 13,257 in 1940 (fewer in 1942-3-4) to 22,819 in 1951. Thus the average money per runner has varied with these two totals - the number of starters and the total amount of money. The average per horse in 1940 was $1,200; in 1947, $2,829; in 1951, $2,434. In 1933 the average was $928.

Instead of using the raw total of dollars earned, I have accepted the annual average per starter as the "expectation" for a runner in any given year, and have restated this expectation as the figure 1. If a runner earned $1,200 in 1940 his index was, of course, 1; if he earned $2,400 in 1940 the index was 2, etc. But if he earned $1,200 in 1947, his index was .42; that is, he earned only 42 per cent of the average money per horse available in North America that year.

It is easy enough to add the totals for individual horses and obtain group indexes, as for the progeny of sires or the progeny of mares. The calculation is simple enough, and I won't take time for it here. It should be enough, at the moment, simply to explain that the index shows the ratio between actual and "expected" earnings. Most sires have progeny indexes below 1. The best have cumulative or lifetime indexes of 4 or more. Here are a few samples of outstanding sires: St. Simon, 4.75; Bull Lea, 4.76 through 1951; Equipoise, 4.43; Blandford, 4.29; Count Fleet, 4.28 through 1951, Hyperion, 4.16 through 1951. Only about 2.5 per cent of sires

46

will have indexes above 2, that is, with earnings twice the normal expectation per starter per year.

I have used this average-earnings index as a measure for the progeny of the mares in this group. It works for mares just the same as for sires, of course.

The data involved are too much to report orally in detail. Some of the detail will be exhibited a little later. At the moment I shall hold mostly to generalities concerning the whole group, and to comparisons of these mares, as producers, with the average of the breed.

All these mares in the group foaled in the years 1930 through 1941 inclusive have had at least one foal to race. (I took the liberty of eliminating at the beginning the mares which I knew had died without producing foals.) This makes a total of 120 mares whose records may be summarized. We might begin at the end, by adding all their records together.

These 120 mares have had a total of 605 living foals, not including two-year-olds of 1952. Through 1951 racing, 529 of these foals had started, or 87.4 per cent. They had earned $13,620,741. This is an average of $22,514 per foal, including the non-runners.

Turning to the use of the average-earnings index, the 529 runners had raced by the end of 1951, a total of 1,605 years, that is, there were 1,605 year-starters. They earned as much as was expected of 5,874 year-starters; 5,874 divided by 1,605 is 3.66 - the average- earnings index for the group. This is to say, they have earned at the rate of $3\frac{2}{3}$ times the normal expectation of the years in which they raced.

This is approximately equal to the lifetime records in America of *Mahmoud and *Heliopolis. If you omit the records of the oldest mares, the group index rises above 4.00, indicating a degree of success which, when attained and held by a stallion, is enough to cause breeders to call him great. Then are these mares, as a group, "great?" I think so. There are some other ways to test.

In order to compute the odds in any given situation you must have what the statisticians call a distribution, by which they mean simply a tally showing the number of cases in each of a number of intervals. We could tally the weights of all the persons in this room, and the result would be a sort of bell-shaped curve with the heaviest person out here on the right and the lightest here on the left. Most of the individual weights would fall in the central area, near the mean. From the curve we could predict, after allowing for a small margin of error, the distribution of the weights of the persons who may gather in this room a year from now. We could not, of course, apply this prediction on an individual basis. We would be unable to predict accurately the weight of, say, the first man to send in an application for the 1953 Short Course from the San Fernando Valley.

In the same way, the Thoroughbred breeder cannot guess very accurately the class or earning capacity of any one unborn foal. But he can make a rather dependable estimate of the class and earning capacity of a group of unborn foals, and this is the important thing for the breeder, to be able to estimate how many good horses he may expect from a given number of foals.

Chapter 7

The Four Plus Horse

A few years ago a young man from North Carolina made it a practice to attend the fall sales at Lexington. He bought mares by the dozen, mostly at prices between $25 and $100. When I inquired as to his plans - meaning, of course, what are you thinking, young man? - he answered that, if he raised, say, a hundred foals, there was bound to be a good one among them somewhere, and with that good one he would pay for all the others. The young man had constructed his own curve of probability and was playing the odds based upon it. Unfortunately, the curve he had constructed was strictly imaginary. Operating as he was, deliberately selecting the worst broodmares (or, at least, the cheapest), he would have been fortunate to get one good horse from a thousand foals.

Before we can study the results from breeding this group of mares selected strictly on the basis of racing class, we shall need some idea of what is the normal expectation from an unselected group of mares, taken at random and representing the average of the breed. If our top mares fail to produce a much larger proportion of good horses than the average of the breed, then we shall have to discard racing class as an indicator of merit in a broodmare.

For this purpose I took two samples, each with a larger number of runners than the group of top race mares had. The samples were taken from my own files, in which I have calculated the average-earnings indexes of the horses which have raced in the last four years. The calculation covers the entire racing career of each of the horses, through 1951, just as in the case of the progeny of the good race mares. The horses are alphabetized under the names of the dams. The first sample began at the beginning at the A's and ran through the produce of Alopatia, a total of 668 horses which made at least one start. The second sample began at the beginning of the C's and ran through Charnot, a total of 812 runners. In the second sample I eliminated the imported horses which ran in North America, because of the possibility that these might tend to distort the results a little. Actually the two samples were so much alike that I added them together and used the full total of 1,480 horses. The distribution will give the basis for calculating the odds - and these are the odds you are playing, provided your breeding stock is no better and no worse than the average of the breed. *(See Table I.)*

(The statisticians would not quite approve of the manner in which I have changed the interval in making this tally. Through the first 16 steps the interval is four-tenths, that is 40 per cent of the continental average per runner for the years raced. After that it is larger. But these figures are made principally for visual comparison, rather than for involved statistical study.)

Now, among these 1,480 runners, how many good horses were there? This raises the question: what is a good horse? That is an arbitrary matter, depending on your particular standards. My own definition of a good horse would exclude a runner

50

Index	BEST MARES		BREED AVERAGE	
	No.	Cum. %	No.	Cum. %
20.00 up	17	100.0	2	100.0
15.00	9	95.5	3	99.7
10.00	19	92.2	5	99.5
9.00	7	91.5	--	
8.00	3	90.2	--	
7.00	8	89.6	4	99.3
6.00	11	88.1	5	99.1
5.60	3	86.0	3	98.7
5.20	9	85.4	3	98.5
4.80	3	83.7	3	98.3
4.40	3	83.2	8	98.1
4.00	6	82.6	7	97.6
3.60	14	81.5	8	97.1
3.20	17	78.8	17	96.6
2.80	15	75.6	18	95.4
2.40	18	72.8	33	94.2
2.00	23	69.4	53	92.0
1.60	44	65.0	80	88.4
1.20	54	56.7	94	83.0
.80	64	46.5	177	76.6
.40	76	34.4	274	64.7
.00	106	20.0	683	46.1

TABLE I. Distribution and cumulative percentages of earnings indexes of (1) progeny of the best race mares and (2) a random sample of 1,480 runners representing the average of the breed.

which fails to earn enough to pay for himself, including cost of production and expense of racing. These expenses will vary with different farms and racing stables, and they also tend to vary, to some extend, along with purses - both the expenses and the purses being a reflection of inflation. Mr. Beard estimates that a horse must win about four times the average (an earnings index of 4) in order to represent a profit for Greentree Farm. Many a horseman seems very happy with a runner which earns twice the average. But no horse in any part of this country is likely to pay his own way at a much lower rate of earnings. An index of 4 - Mr. Beard's standard for Greentree - is roughly the equivalent to stakes class. Many stakes winners - about half of them, at a guess - have a lower rate of earning. Outstanding race horses may have indexes above 20.

Whatever your standards of excellence, you will see from the percentile table that three out of every four horses bred and raced in North America have an index of less than 1.20. Now, a horse which earns no more than 20 per cent above the continental average can be set down as a liability, as a race horse, that is. (A filly which earns as much as the average is a pretty good broodmare prospect.)

You will note that 2.9 per cent - say, roughly, three out of a hundred runners - earn as much as four times the average. This is, or was, a few years ago, about the percentage of stakes winners that could be expected in any given crop of foals. But the proportion of stakes to the total number of races and the total number of horses tends to vary from time to time. Hence I think that a "four-plus" index, as we might call it, has become a more dependable hallmark of merit than a stakes victory.

Going a little further up the scale of merit, we find that less than one per cent of the horses racing earn as much as seven times the average (these are horses like Challtack and Hank H., for instance), and only about one-tenth of one per cent earn 20 times the average - actually two out of 1,480, or one in 740.

Now let's see how the produce of the best race mares are distributed along the same scale of merit. Note first that only 46.5 per cent of them have racing indexes of less than 1.20, as compared with 76.6 per cent of the average-of-the-breed group, which of course includes some good mares, as well as many poor ones. Then note that 35 per cent earn at least twice the average; this is $3\frac{1}{2}$ times the proportion of two-plus runners in the average of the breed.

The further you go toward the top of the scale of merit, the more pronounced is the superiority of the offspring of the best race mares. Take the seven-plus mark, for instance. In the whole breed the expectancy is .9 per cent, slightly less than one in a hundred; among the produce of the top race mares, the expectancy is 11.9 per cent. At this point, the good race mares produce 13 times as many good horses as may be expected from the average of the breed. (See also Table II.) Among the 1,480 runners in the average sample were two horses which earned more than 20 times the normal expectation. Among

INDEX	BEST RACE MARES	AVERAGE OF BREED
.00 to .39	20.0%	46.1%
.40 to .79	14.4	18.6
.80 to 1.19	12.1	11.9
1.20 to 1.99	18.5	11.8
2.00 to 3.99	16.5	8.7
4.00 to 9.99	10.0	2.2
10.00 plus	8.5	.7
	100.0	100.0

TABLE II. Distribution, in percentages at various levels of excellence, of (1) progeny of the best race mares and (2) a random sample of 1,480 runners.

the 529 runners from the top race mares there were 17 horses in this class. The comparison at this point is between .13 per cent and 3.2 per cent. That is to say, the probability of an outstanding runner from a top race mare is about 25 times the probability of an outstanding runner from a mare taken at random.

I submit that no one has ever devised a method of evaluating pedigrees which will yield such a margin of superiority - and that no one is ever likely to do so.

Since statistics may be dull and less convincing than specific example, I have made a list of the four-plus runners produced by this group of leading race mares. If examples make a deeper impression on your mind than a statistical curve, here is some added evidence of the superiority of good race mares as producers. (See Table III.)

Here are 105 horses of stakes class (including the 1952 developments One Count, Ancestor, Real Delight, Mark-Ye-Well, and Navy Page, but excluding 17 stakes winners which failed to win four times the average) - approximately one high-class runner from every five foals to reach the races. If you exclude 1952 racing, there are 18.5 per cent four-plus horses in the group of 529 runners. This is a proportion greater than the usual expectation from the best sire in the country.

In the group are 34 runners which had earned $100,000 before the end of 1951, at least three others which have earned $100,000 this year, and one which earned the equivalent of $100,000 in England. It is inconceivable that anyone excluding racing ability from his standards for selecting broodmare prospects could equal this record.

Dam, year foaled	Offspring, year foaled, sire	Earnings	Index
Ace Card, 1942	POST CARD, 1947, Firethorn	$119,375	17.14
	YILDIZ, 1948, *Mahmoud	69,825	14.41
	ONE COUNT, 1949, Count Fleet		
Anthemion, 1940	BRYAN G., 1947, *Blenheim II	104,425	14.43
Apogee, 1934	FLOOD TOWN, 1942, Johnstown	116,710	5.86
Bala Ormont, 1936	BE FLEET, 1947, Count Fleet	122,475	16.83
Bazaar, 1931	BEST SELLER, 1938, Blue Larkspur	53,235	7.13
Bee Mac, 1941	BETTER SELF, 1945, Bimelech	383,925	37.27
	PROPHETS THUMB, 1946, Bull Lea	44,012	6.07
	MAC BEA, 1950, Bimelech		
Big Hurry, 1936	BE FEARLESS, 1942, Burgoo King	88,980	4.30
	BRIDAL FLOWER, 1943, *Challenger II	222,055	20.06
	THE ADMIRAL, 1946, War Admiral	37,225	13.84
Black Wave, 1935	JET PILOT, 1944, *Blenheim II	198,740	35.29
Bloodroot, 1932	BRIC A BAC, 1941, War Admiral	103,225	8.62
	BE FAITHFUL, 1942, Bimelech	189,040	17.07
	ANCESTOR, 1949, Challedon		
Blue Delight, 1938	ALL BLUE, 1947, Bull Lea	81,960	11.61
	REAL DELIGHT, 1949, Bull Lea		
	BUBBLEY, 1950, Bull Lea		
Broad Ripple, 1934	RIPPEY, 1943, Pompey	299,155	27.96
Catalysis, 1935	MRS. AMES, 1941, Johnstown	55,805	9.91
Ciencia, 1936	CURANDERO, 1946, Brazado	238,650	25.09
Cocopet, 1941	PUT OUT, 1949, Shut Out	18,525	7.61
Columbiana, 1933	OCEAN WAVE, 1940, *Blenheim II	37,825	7.76
	FREE AMERICA, 1945, *Blenheim II	51,266	7.62
Creole Maid, 1935	NATCHEZ, 1943, Jamestown	166,845	11.92
Dark Discovery, 1938	HULL DOWN, 1948, Count Fleet	25,670	5.35
Dinner Date, 1936	MENU, 1943, *Bahram	76,150	4.17
Donita M., 1936	DONITAS FIRST, 1941, Reaping Reward	43,565	9.84
Esposa, 1932	ESTEEM, 1942, Stimulus	29,935	6.65
Fair Weather, 1940	AMERICAN GLORY, 1946, Roman	43,495	4.53
Farmerette, 1940	MISS MOMMY, 1945, *Bull Dog	81,825	10.14
	BULLY BOY, 1947, *Bull Dog	29,475	4.12
Far Star, 1931	STAR REWARD, 1944, Reaping Reward	182,275	17.38
	FLEETING STAR, 1946, Count Fleet	35,901	5.09
	SABAEAN, 1947, Challedon	24,075	9.89
Ficklebush, 1939	FABEROSE, 1949, Rosemont	10,200	4.19
Floradora, 1933	STAR PILOT, 1943, *Sickle	187,855	27.10
Forever Yours, 1933	MAHMOUDESS, 1942, *Mahmoud	95,312	7.15
	ETERNAL REWARD, 1943, Reaping Reward	194,285	14.04
	STEADFAST, 1948, *Mahmoud	30,125	6.28
Good Morning, 1940	BATTLE MORN, 1948, *Blenheim II	60,475	13.03
Handcuff, 1935	CHAINS, 1945, Firethorn	95,200	9.59
Imperatrice, 1938	SCATTERED, 1945, Whirlaway	80,275	9.91
	SQUARED AWAY, 1947, *Piping Rock	42,825	9.09
Iseult, 1930	MERRY LASSIE, 1935, Stimulus	41,320	16.65
	NAVIGATING, 1940, Hard Tack	18,117	4.04

Dam	Produce	Earnings	Index
	EASY WHIRL, 1948, Whirlaway	25,825	5.48
Jabot, 1931	COUNTERPOINT, 1948, Count Fleet	251,225	51.62
Jacola, 1935	PHALANX, 1944, Pilate	409,235	36.62
Light Lady, 1939	KIT CARSON, 1946, He Did	52,560	5.45
Little Risk, 1937	RISK A WHIRL, 1946, Whirlaway	57,720	8.18
Manatella, 1934	SALMAGUNDI, 1945, Hash	166,795	15.50
Mar-Kell, 1939	MARK-YE-WELL, 1949, Bull Lea		
Mata Hari, 1931	SPY SONG, 1943, Balladier	206,325	19.72
Miss Bunting, 1930	OCCUPATION, 1940, *Bull Dog	227,035	50.47
	OCCUPY, 1941, *Bull Dog	217,214	21.67
Miss Dogwood, 1939	RIOT, 1945, Whirlaway	61,955	5.31
	SEQUENCE, 1946, Count Fleet	54,850	10.36
	BERNWOOD, 1948, *Bernborough	53,935	11.42
	BELLA FIGURA, 1949, Count Fleet	10,850	4.46
Miss Dolphin, 1934	OLYMPIA, 1946, *Heliopolis	365,632	49.95
Miss Ferdinand, 1937	SEA SNACK, 1943, Hard Tack	127,400	15.63
Miss Merriment, 1931	STUNTS, 1945, *Hypnotist II	81,305	6.69
Misty Isle, 1938	COSMIC MISSILE, 1944, Roman	121,150	14.37
Motto, 1932	MR. TROUBLE, 1947, *Mahmoud	71,225	10.34
Mrs. Ames, 1941	PICTUS, 1948, Pictor	40,440	8.62
Myrtlewood, 1932	MISS DOGWOOD, 1939, *Bull Dog	31,712	7.37
	DURAZNA, 1941, Bull Lea	70,201	11.53
Nasca, 1938	BIG IF, 1945, King Cole	70,780	5.48
Nellie Flag, 1932	MAR-KELL, 1939, *Blenheim II	84,365	12.26
	NELLIE L. , 1940, *Blenheim II	20,295	6.24
Nellie L., 1940	DE LUXE, 1946, Bull Lea	56,785	6.24
	JENNIE LEE, 1948, Bull Lea	14,160	5.82
Now What, 1937	NEXT MOVE, 1947, Bull Lea	306,725	45.18
Our Page, 1940	PAGE BOOTS, 1945, Our Boots	51,635	6.38
	SPORT PAGE, 1946, Our Boots	79,175	14.80
	BULL PAGE, 1947, Bull Lea	25,730	5.41
	NAVY PAGE, 1947, War Admiral		
Painted Veil, 1938	MOHAMMEDAN, 1948, *Mahmoud	25,900	5.70
Petrify, 1939	STONE AGE, 1946, *Bahram	53,550	5.32
Piquet, 1937	CAPOT, 1946, Menow	345,260	46.47
Roseretter, 1935	SERVICE PILOT, 1942, Pilate	124,750	6.12
	ROSE BEAM, 1945, *Blenheim II	74,605	6.10
Rosetown, 1937	HIGH TREND, 1944, Jack High	102,885	6.84
Salaminia, 1937	ATHENIA, 1943, *Pharamond II	105,710	12.64
	AEGINA, 1947, Sir Damion	42,400	6.28
Some Pomp, 1931	PROUD ONE, 1938, *Blenheim II	22,720	4.19
	SOME CHANCE, 1939, Chance Play	180,735	28.02
	BEAU DANDY, 1945, Bull Lea	52,055	5.30
	DUCHESS PEG, 1947, Whirlaway	67,727	14.14
Split Second, 1933	SONIC, 1948, Blue Larkspur	25,350	5.25
Tangled, 1938	TAILSPIN, 1944, *Blenheim II	43,300	7.66
Too Timely, 1940	SAFE ARRIVAL, 1945, Eight Thirty	61,030	4.93
Toro Nancy, 1932	BOSWELL LADY, 1945, *Boswell	50,775	9.12
	TWO AND TWENTY, 1946, Gallant Duke	46,775	4.91
Twilight Tear 1941	A GLEAM, 1949, *Blenheim II	56,345	23.15

Two Bob, 1933	TWOSY, 1942, Bull Lea	101,375	10.09
	TWO LEA, 1946, Bull Lea	134,700	19.39
Unerring, 1936	FAULTLESS, 1944, Bull Lea	304,945	27.61
Vagrancy, 1939	BLACK TARQUIN, 1945, *Rhodes Scholar (£25,328)		55.67
	VULCANIA, 1948, Some Chance	54,815	11.77
War Date, 1942	JET'S DATE, 1949, Jet Pilot	10,900	4.48
White Lies, 1930	PREVARICATOR, 1943, Omaha	147,300	7.95

TABLE III. Earnings and indexes, through 1951, of best progeny of best race mares. Indexes above 4.00 included. Absence of figures in earnings and index columns indicates horses which gained first distinction in 1952.

Chapter 8

Increasing the Odds of Breeding a Stake's Winner

Probabilities sometimes can be better understood if they are reduced to specific numbers. Suppose you have a hundred broodmares. You have picked them up here and there, some because they were "well bred," some because they were cheap, some because they were good-looking, etc. Let us say you have approximated the average of the breed. You maintain the stud at this level long enough to breed a thousand foals that get to the races - that would take twenty-odd years. What are we to expect from these thousand runners?

For the answer, simply look at the distribution for the average of the breed (Table I, page 51), which includes the progeny of the best race mares as well as others. You can write off 750 of them at once as a big waste of money, horses which will not come anywhere near paying their expenses. You can expect another 200 to win approximately enough to pay their training costs, but not enough extra to account for what it cost to breed and raise them. That leaves about 50 horses with the job of making up the deficit on the other 950. In order to get the operation in the black, they will have to earn money at a rate which is far beyond their capacity. About seven of them will earn as much as ten times the

INDEX	BEST RACE MARES	AVERAGE OF BREED	RATIO
2.00	4	12	1:3
4.00	8	48	1:6
10.00	16	200	1:12
20.00	44	1,076	1:24

TABLE IV. Number of mares which must be maintained in order to produce each year, on the average, one runner of a given earning capacity or better, assuming that 1.4 mares will produce annually one foal which gets to the races. Note that the ratio increases geometrically. That is, the relative number of average-of-the-breed mares required to equal the producing record of the top-class race mares is doubled with each upward step in the scale of excellence as given here. Note also the interesting progressions in the actual numbers. (It is patterns of this sort which suggests the possibility that geneticist might use the average-earnings index to create fairly simple formulas for the use of breeders in estimating probabilities.

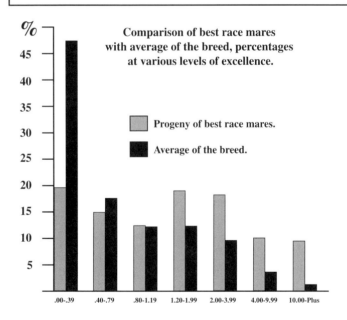

Comparison of best race mares with average of the breed, percentages at various levels of excellence.

Progeny of best race mares.

Average of the breed.

average, and one or two will earn 20 times the average. Suppose, on the other hand, that you were endowed with such charm, such luck, and such a bank account that you could maintain for 20 years a stud in which all the mares came from among the best ten race mares of the years in which they were foaled. You would have to write off 465 as racing losses - or possibly 300 if you bred only to high-ranking sires. You would have, at the other end of the scale, 185 horses of good stakes class - not just plain stakes class. And you would have about 32 runners of outstanding merit, horses such as Counterpoint, Phalanx, Capot, Black Tarquin, Jet Pilot, Better Self, Spy Song, Rippey, Occupation, Olympia, One Count, Mark-Ye-Well, etc., mares like Real Delight, Next Move, Bridal Flower, A Gleam, Two Lea, etc., etc. Long before your 20 years was up, you would have broken all the records in history for the production of high-class horses by a single stud farm.

Suppose, to take it another way, you fix your goal as the production of one high-class (four-plus) horse a year. Assuming that about 70 per cent of your matings will produce horses which get to the races, you can breed, on the average, one good stakes winner per year from a stud of eight mares. (Table IV.)

(Actually, a little less than 40 per cent of matings will produce horses which get to the races. The numbers of mares given in the tables and illustrations are too low, but the proportions between the two groups are not affected by substituting 40 per cent for 70 per cent.)

But, if you breed from an unselected group of mares and stallions, you must maintain a stud of about 48 mares in order to expect one fairly good stakes-class horse per year. Automatically it is going to cost you six times as much, year in and year out, to pay the expenses incident to the production of this one good horse.

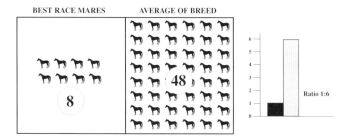

To produce annually one runner with an index of 4.00

Suppose, further, that you are not satisfied with one four-plus horse a year, but wish to produce every year one which earns as much as ten times the average. You can do this with 16 top-class race mares. But if you think racing class is unimportant and that any mare is equally likely to produce a ten-plus runner, then you will need a stud of 200 mares in order to get the one a year which was your goal.

Note especially - for this is the key to the whole problem - the manner in which the odds have shifted here. If your standard is a good winner, say a horse which earns twice the annual average, you need a little more than three times as many average mares as good racers. If you want a horse of fairly good

62

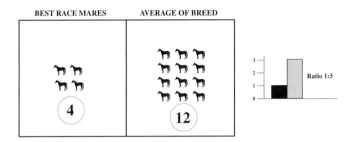

To produce annually one runner with an index of 2.00

stakes class (four-plus), it will take six times as many unselected mares. If you want genuinely good stakes class (ten-plus), it will take 12½ times as many unselected mares as good race mares. If your goal is outstanding runners (20-plus), the classic winners and top handicap horses, then the odds are 24 to 1 in favor of the top-class race mare.

This is a very steep progression. It means, certainly, that the higher your standards are, the more essential it is for you to accept racing class as a basis for judging a broodmare prospect. It means also, I think, that the probability of excellence as a producer rises in accordance with excellence as a runner all the way to the very top class. There is no point at which, as many breeders have thought, a mare has too much class for her own good as a producer.

Chapter 9

Rating Sires

Thus far, in attempting to emphasize the importance of the individual as the basis for selecting breeding stock, I have confined the discussion to the records of mares. Inevitably the question will rise in your mind: Were not these high-class race mares successful mainly because they were mated with good sires? I think the question can be answered satisfactorily.

In an effort to get at this problem I took the 529 runners from this group of mares and arranged them according to their sires. Then, rather arbitrarily, I studied the records of all the runners whose sires were represented by at least four starters. This does not of course eliminate all the sires which you might designate as unsuccessful. A few of the stallions included are definitely unsuccessful. However, such a sorting does fine down the quality of the stallions to some extent; it represents, at least, what the owners of the mares thought were the most acceptable mates for their good runners. I have preferred this simple method of selection simply because, if I had attempted to judge between the successful and the unsuccessful sires, I would have been taking advantage of hindsight. The owners of the mares could only make their best guesses as to the future of these stallions, and that future in most cases now has become the past.

If I have justified the method sufficiently, the results are easy enough. Whenever these top race mares were mated with prominent sires, the runners from these matings were, on the average, superior to the whole group. This was to be expected. They were superior to the other progeny of the same mares. But they were also greatly superior, on the average, to the other progeny of the same sires.

In order to save a little time, let us call the runners by the supposedly good sires out of these mares Group A. The other runners from the same mares we will call Group B. Some of those in Group B will be by good sires also - and of course. Now, are there any significant differences between Group A and B? Here are the results; you can judge for yourselves.

Group	Runners	Above 4.00	Above 10.0
A	376	81 (21.5%)	39 (10.4%)
B	153	17 (11.1%)	6 (3.9%)
Total	529	98 (18.5%)	45 (8.5%)

You will see at once that Group A is greatly superior to B. It has more than twice as large a proportion of horses of stakes class (four-plus) as does Group B. When you move up to a still higher standard (ten-plus), the difference is even more pronounced.

If we were to exercise a little hindsight and eliminate a few of the sires which actually were not good enough for these mares, there would be a still greater difference.

The average-earnings index for Group A through 1951 was 4.39. For Group B it was 2.15.

However, it hardly seems necessary at this point to dwell upon the already well-known fact that you get better results from breeding to good sires than others. What I am trying to demonstrate is the less well known and more important fact that you get better results breeding from good race mares than from mares which were not good athletes themselves.

An even 50 sires are accounted for in Group A. In 33 cases Group A has a higher average-earnings index for the sire concerned than the life-time index of the sire. In 17 cases the sire's record would have been better if he had never been mated with any of these mares. The proportion here is 2 to 1 in favor of the good race mares.

If you take the larger sub-groups in Group A, there are 11 sires which have had as many as 10 runners each from these mares. The good race mares have improved the records of nine of these, the only exceptions being *Sir Gallahad III (represented by nine fillies among 12 runners) and Sweep All. Here is the comparison of the records in Group A with the full records of the stallions represented by as many as 10 runners in Group A:

Whirlaway

Sire	Runners	4.00	Group Index	Sire's Index
* Bahram	11	2	2.31	2.07
* Blenheim II	26	11	5.48	2.71
* Bull Dog	19	5	6.16	2.34
Bull Lea	21	11	8.93	4.76
Count Fleet	16	6	8.08	4.28
Johnstown	11	2	3.58	1.24
* Mahmoud	12	5	5.13	3.63
* Sir Gallahad III	12	--	.97	1.92
Sweep All	10	--	.92	1.24
War Admiral	12	2	3.72	3.03
Whirlaway	23	5	2.95	2.37

Here again is an example of what might be called a parlay effect. The good race mares we have been studying have improved the over-all record of this group of good sires. And you may notice the suggestion of a pattern: the more successful the stallion, the more likely is it that such mares will increase the margin of this success. Note especially the tremendously high indexes for the offspring of Bull Lea and Count Fleet from this group of mares. Most of *Blenheim II's progeny in this group were got after he was 16 years old, yet the group index is a trifle more than twice the lifetime index of *Blenheim II's progeny in North America. (By way of postscript I might call attention to the fact that the 1952 records of Mark-Ye-Well, Real Delight and One Count are not included in the above figures for Bull Lea and Count Fleet.)

No one will assume, I hope, that I am attempting to persuade anyone to breed only from top-class race mares. There are some situations - as, for instance, when prices for such mares are inflated out of proportion to their actual prospects - when it would be very poor policy to buy such mares. I have taken this group with exceptional racing class only to demonstrate the overwhelming importance of the individual and the relative unimportance of the pedigree.

In actual experience, good broodmares frequently develop from mares which were not raced at all or which raced without distinction. And of course some of the best race mares fail as producers, for one reason or another. In Thoroughbred breeding, as I have remarked elsewhere, gold is where you find it, but the best place to look is right on the surface - in the individual itself, in the phenotype.

In choosing broodmares on the basis of racing class, it is important to remember always that we must try a great many mares, whereas we should be willing to gamble on only a few stallions, nearly all of them from the top one per cent in racing class. Hence we should study the racing performances of many mares. If a breeder expects to be successful, I think he would be well advised to prefer the top 10 per cent of the race mares in selecting his breeding stock: this would include mares with racing indexes down to about 1.80. If he goes regularly below the top 25 per cent (which would include indexes down to about 1.00), he is inviting failure. It should be possible, without paying high prices, to assemble a group of good broodmare prospects from mares with racing indexes between 1.00 and 3.00. Many of these will be selling platers, but a good plater is a good breeding prospect.

Many of our outstanding race horses have come from mares which were poor racers, say, somewhere in the bottom 60 per cent. The mechanism of heredity is arranged like any other game of chance: the improbable sometimes happens. But if you will study carefully the origins of these improbable champions, you will only occasionally find that they could have been predicted on the basis of pedigree.

Chapter 10

Miscellaneous Thoughts on Breeding

Broodmare Sires

Many breeders insist that a broodmare should be the daughter of a "good broodmare sire." They may be willing to pay a high price for a mare simply because she is a daughter of *Sir Gallahad III, or Man o'War, or Hyperion, for instance. This is another extravagance to be indulged by those who can afford it. The correlation between grandparent and grandchild is nearly nil. It is difficult enough to estimate the odds for one generation ahead. It is virtually impossible to compound the odds for two generations and have much expectancy of an accurate estimate.

The important thing here, as everywhere else, is the individual. Some sires, of course, get more good individuals than others. In the main the good individuals will be the ones which make the reputation of a broodmare sire.

Male Sires

There is a strong tendency for breeders to set up certain idols among the names they find in pedigrees, such as Bend Or, St. Simon, Domino, *Teddy, Hyperion, etc., and this emphasis becomes almost worshipful when it concerns a "strong" male line.

Hyperion

The same generalization - that it is the individual which is important - applies here. There is no dependability in male lines as such. It is, in general, the best sons of the best sires which carry on the line. The fact that a young stallion is a son of a successful sire adds almost nothing to his chances for success.

One whole system of breeding, the Vuillier theory of dosages, has been founded upon this undue emphasis upon the more prominent names in pedigrees. There is not time to discuss the question fully, but the conclusions, like all conclusions based on the pedigrees of good horses, only are erroneous.

Families

There are also idols on the distaff side, and here again a system of breeding has been established, that of Bruce Lowe. Some breeders still insist that a sire should come from a "sire family," that is, a family which has produced prominent sires. The emptiness of this theory has been exposed a thousand times.

Inbreeding

There are all sorts of pedigree patterns, such as those of Vuillier and Bruce Lowe. One with a persistent fascination for breeders is inbreeding or linebreeding. I can only report that I know of no instance in which it could be demonstrated that inbreeding in the Thoroughbred has produced results appreciably better or worse than could have been expected from the same sires and dams on the basis of their individual merit.

In fixing the type of the origins of any breed, inbreeding plays a considerable role, and it did so when the race horse was being established as a breed. But we are no longer breeding for a type. We are breeding for the extremes of speed and stamina. In modern competition, inbreeding is no better and no worse than outcrossing; the result of any mating is determined in the main by the two parents, and only in a negligible degree by their ancestors.

Nicks

By far the most persistent pedigree pattern is the so-called nick, or fortunate combination of bloodlines. It has never been the basis of a formalized system, but is accepted by many, and perhaps most, breeders as a part of nature, like oats and pasture. We have always had nicks, from the days of Herod and Eclipse down to the days of Blue Larkspur and Bull Lea.

The theory of nicks is that a special combination of bloodlines will, of itself, add something to the expectancy from a given mating. If you were breeding paramecia or fruit flies, or possibly laboratory mice, there would be instances in which nicks would be found useful in producing the result desired. But in any animal whose excellence depends upon so involved a mechanism of heredity as the race horse, they are altogether useless. The result from any given mating will depend upon the parents, and not upon any conceivable combination of bloodlines.

Signs

We have an instrument of policy-making left over to us from the Old Stone Age, or thereabouts. Horsemen in central Kentucky are among the last surviving believers in an ancient doctrine that whatever one does should be done when the sign is right. The doctrine has been stripped of most of its ritual, and its origin and supernatural basis are all but lost in the mists of ten thousand years. The last of the priest-kings who might have understood why it was best, for instance, to wean when the sign was below the knees, must have died in the bronze age when Bel and Marduk were in their dotage and mortality was running high among the gods of old.

Sometimes I have argued that the sign is no longer an effective guide for weaning, castration, and such; because the earth has an inconstant relationship to the heavens, the astrological sign has slipped a few cogs, and the constellation of Aries the Ram is now where Pisces the Fish was two thousand years ago (or vice versa), and it is no longer possible to tell heads from tails. The sign, in short, is out of date, and there has been no investigation to

74

determine whether the head is better than the feet. It is doubtful whether any policy, even the policy of a horse breeder as to when weaning should be undertaken, should be based upon a body of knowledge to which nothing has been added for two thousand years, at least.

The sign we can let be, except as a symbol of the areas in which we have been content to "let well enough alone," to make do with a little knowledge and much folklore, and even to lose some of the wisdom of our ancestors. The late Alex B. Gordon used to say that one improvement in racing had been made during his lifetime: the protective skull cap for jockeys. Leaving aside the field of veterinary science, we have not gained much. We have been so preoccupied with image that we have neglected substance.

Summary

Pedigrees are useful only when we are ignorant of the merit of the individual, and not very useful then. The more we know about the individual and its progeny, the less we need to know about the pedigree. When we have a moderately complete record of the individual and its progeny, the pedigree becomes useless.

Chapter 11

The Blood-Horse Compendium

Joe Estes edited *The Blood-Horse* for 28 years. As is the case with most magazines of modest circulation, the title of "Editor" was somewhat misleading. It implied that his role was the supervision of a staff of writers, assigning projects to each and tweaking the work product before it was published.

In practice, the job of *The Blood-Horse* editor was far less glamorous. Estes wrote much of what appeared in each edition. On the other hand, the magazine gave Estes a ready forum in which to air his views on breeding and racing.

This chapter is a compendium of some of Estes' more provocative observations gleaned from the pages of *The Blood-Horse* during his tenure.

"There are four substantial barriers to the improvement of the Thoroughbred breed in the United States: (1) The extreme prevalence of claiming racing; (2) the lack of distance racing; (3) the lack of adequate racing for fillies, and (4) the blind refusal of breeders as a group to rid themselves of their least successful stock."

June 21, 1941

"Bruce Lowe's theory that certain hereditary excellencies and deficiencies descended in unimpaired vigor through many generations of females was one of the most absurd notions ever thrust into the welcoming arms of Thoroughbred breeders."

March 8, 1935

"I am afraid that the comparative ages of sires and dams offer no worthwhile clues to the mystery of how to breed good horses."

April 7, 1934

"When a young horse enters the stud he should be judged, first, by his class as a racer; second, by his physical attributes; third, by his pedigree."

November 10, 1934

"What is here set forth is the shadow of a dream in that it envisions a creation the like of which has not been seen in America. But hard mathematics, solid common sense, substantial facts, and the integrity of a community give substance and form to the dream. Here are set forth the mathematics and the facts for the consideration of those who would have the dream come true. It is our desire that lovers of the Thoroughbred throughout the country will recognize in this a serious effort to establish a model race track, to perpetuate racing in the proper manner and to provide a course which will stand for many years as a symbol of the fine traditions of the sport. In order to accomplish these ends, we shall first ask the aid of sportsmen in building the track. Later we shall ask them to race their horses and to lend their own presence at the meetings. We shall ask the good will and active cooperation of many, for this is an enterprise which, if it proves successful, will be an everlasting credit to the sport of racing, not only in Kentucky, but throughout America."

From the prospectus for
the Keeneland Association, 1935

"The average stakes-winning broodmare may be said to have produced exactly three times as many stakes winners as the non-stakes-winning broodmare."

December 7, 1935

"Younger stallions have no advantage over old stallions, except in number of progeny."

September 26, 1936

"The racing record of a mare is the best single index to her probable worth as a producer."

April 3, 1937

"The better racer a mare is, the better her producing record will be, on the average."

January 8, 1938

"The reason I keep harping on the subject of good race mares as good producers is to fix the point that in breeding Thoroughbreds, the most important consideration is the test of the race course, and that race tracks are doing a service to the breeder and to the sport in general if they offer a good number of races exclusively for fillies and mares."

January 29, 1938

"Coat color is no clue to anything except coat color."

May 15, 1937

"No nick is necessary for a good horse."

August 20, 1938

"The breeder who leans on a male line rather than on a prepotent individual is trusting a broken reed."

February 25, 1939

"In choosing your breeding stock, look first for racing class. And don't be afraid to pay for racing class. It is a good investment."

March 5, 1939

"The conclusion remains unshaken that the value of a mare as a producer is in direct proportion to her class as a racer, and no better standard for choosing a broodmare is available to the breeder, however long he may pore over pedigrees."

April 15, 1939

"Distance racing is a much better test for breeding material than sprint racing is."

February 10, 1940

"Our slavish following of speed and snubbing of stamina has eliminated the best standard we ever had for judging breeding stock, especially broodmares, and therefore, has eliminated the best means we ever had for improving the breed of horses."

October 12, 1940

"It has not been demonstrated that a correlation of any practical significance to the Thoroughbred breeder, exists between inbreeding and prepotence."

January 2, 1943

"Make the best possible estimate of the individual and its parents and you will never find it necessary to worry about birthrank."

December 4, 1943

"The American Turf has given up distance racing and substituted two-year-old racing in its stead."

October 12, 1940

"The Bruce Lowe family number is worth no more to the breeder than the horoscope he gets when he puts a penny in one of those drugstore weighing machines."

February 3,1945

"Pedigrees are useful only when we are ignorant of the merit of the individual and not very useful then. The more we know about the individual and its progeny the less we need to know about the pedigree. When we have a moderately complete record of the individual and its progeny, the pedigree becomes useless."

November 29, 1952

The number of crosses of some great ancestor in a pedigree is of no consequence whatever. Poor horses and good horses have the same number of crosses."

February 3, 1945

"In general, the best sires are those which were possessed of stamina as well as speed. Nearly all the important stud successes will be made by horses which could run at least nine furlongs, and the great majority by those which could go farther. There will always be a few speed horses among the prominent sires, but the odds against the good sprinter are much greater - even in this speed crazy country - than against the horse possessed of both speed and stamina."

December 8, 1951

"There is no evidence that hard racing has an adverse effect upon the quality of a mare's production, except insofar as it keeps her out of production in her best, youngest years."

June 6, 1953

"The fault lies in the sophistry that all drugs must be considered stimulants or depressants...Would it not be better if the commissioners relieved themselves of the obligation to maintain a doctrine which they cannot square with reality?"

July 8, 1961

"Nicks are the bunk. They are the most universally accepted bunk in the whole business."

February 3, 1945

"Repeat and interval running, not necessarily in the rudimentary form Wyndham Walden used, but refined on the basis of human experience, almost certainly would result in an improvement in equine athletic feats."

November 18, 1961

"It reminds us of the race track, where any self-respecting tout can do better selling his advice than betting on it. And of the yearling market, where it is so much more blessed to give than to receive that the amateurs outnumber the professionals in the business of giving advice."

July 22, 1961

"There is no fun in staring with a codfish eye at a yearling and being so ignorant as to discover no fine points worthy of recording, in cryptic scrawl on the catalogue page. There is, on the other hand, an unexplainable sort of pleasure to be derived from the intellectual pursuit of making judgments, predictions, and perhaps bids, on the basis of the knowledgeable study of a youngster's conformation and action."

July 22, 1961

"The scientific basis for banning phenylbutazone is that it might stimulate a horse? In massive doses it can kill a horse - that makes it a stimulant? (asked Alice of the Old Racing Commissioner.) Not necessarily. But certainly it's a pain reliever. You have to admit that a dead horse feels no pain."

December 2, 1961

"The difficulty with the handicap in America is not in the range of weights, which is too narrow rather than too broad, but in the extremely limited range of distance."

October 14, 1961

"There is nothing like a positive opinion - right or wrong - about the future of a race horse to shore up one's confidence in his judgment."

July 22, 1961

"For the first American breeder who finds himself able to ignore pedigrees entirely and to select his broodmares solely on the basis of apparent or demonstrated racing class, and I don't mean stakes-winning class exclusively, I am going to predict an unqualified success."

January 18, 1941

"In the wonderful world of horse racing, the side effects of drugs sometimes are less noticeable in the reactions of the animal under treatment than in the logic of the men who sit in judgment."

December 2, 1961

"In the beginning, a dope was a narcotic. A narcotic was a stimulant. A stimulant became a medication that tended to restore the health of an ailing horse. A medication became a substance which affected the racing condition of a horse in a race. Ergo, a substance which affected the racing condition of a horse in a race became dope."

August 4, 1962

"A good broodmare sire is a good sire. A poor sire is not going to be a good broodmare sire."

February 3, 1945

84

"The value of information lies in its application to procedure and policy. Application depends upon availability, and availability in many applications depends upon speed in today's increasingly complicated world, speed, depends upon automation. And racing eventually must depend upon automation for the feedback of information necessary for determination of sound procedure and sound policy. The question is not so much whether we should make use of automation as how long we can afford to do without it."

August 5, 1951

Appendix I

Thoroughbred Season Earnings

Listed on following page are the official *Daily Racing Form* season average earnings for the years 1985-1997 for all North American performances.

To determine the Average Earnings Index (AEI) for a horse, divide the horse's earnings for that year by the corresponding average earnings for the horse.

For example, a 1985 Thoroughbred that earned $7,900 has an AEI for that year of 1.0 ($7,900 horse's earnings, divided by breed average of $7,900 = 1.0). A two-year-old that earned $15,800 has an AEI of 2.0.

Average the AEI for each year the horse performed to determine its lifetime AEI.

Thoroughbred Average Earnings

Year	Average Earnings
1985	$7,900
1986	7,812
1987	7,952
1988	8,199
1989	8,483
1990	8,693
1991	9,747
1992	10,020
1993	10,315
1994	10,321
1995	11,209
1996	12,022
1997	12,854

* Annual earnings courtesy of The Daily Racing Form

Appendix II

Standardbred Season Earnings

Listed on following pages are the official USTA season average earnings for the years 1985-1997 for all North American performances including Canada. The average earnings are broken down by gait and age for each season.

To determine the Average Earnings Index (AEI) for a horse, divide the horse's earnings for that year by the corresponding average earnings for age of the horse.

For example, a 1985 two-year-old trotter that earned $9,706 has an AEI for that year of 1.0 ($9,706 horse's earnings, divided by breed average of $9,706 = 1.0). A two-year-old that earned $19,412 has an AEI of 2.0.

Average the AEI for each year the horse performed to determine its lifetime AEI.

Season Earnings for Pacers

Age	1985	1986	1987	1988	1989	1990	1991	1992	1993	1994	1995	1996	1997
2	$6,311	6,510	6,153	6,532	6,661	6,755	6,705	6,717	6,400	6,996	7,360	7,758	8,229
3	7,572	7,816	8,037	8,248	8,570	8,668	8,618	9,230	9,060	9,842	10,699	11,023	11,881
4	7,176	7,673	7,565	8,054	8,699	8,428	8,043	8,284	8,492	9,286	10,313	9,997	10,717
5	7,075	7,187	7,852	7,970	8,228	8,714	8,016	8,391	8,019	8,924	10,639	10,857	11,001
6	6,427	6,412	6,772	7,358	7,269	7,370	7,409	7,333	7,600	7,738	9,068	10,451	10,816
7	5,615	5,526	5,919	6,119	6,699	6,436	6,216	6,796	6,443	6,851	7,886	8,591	9,793
8	4,612	4,645	5,101	5,109	5,436	5,686	5,547	5,435	5,999	5,553	6,651	7,433	7,924
9	3,792	3,776	4,014	4,341	4,185	4,402	4,556	4,909	4,663	5,072	5,127	6,128	6,931
10	3,251	3,376	3,291	3,462	3,525	3,745	3,568	3,928	4,085	4,375	4,746	4,484	5,572
11	2,533	2,749	2,870	3,101	2,987	3,207	2,914	3,072	3,357	3,399	3,913	4,673	4,876
12	2,351	2,310	2,171	2,667	2,588	2,649	2,779	2,438	2,612	3,012	3,326	4,468	3,363
13	2,196	1,894	1,800	1,744	2,170	2,300	2,218	1,853	1,851	1,925	2,129	2,605	4,286
14	2,154	1,831	2,315	2,239	1,966	1,630	1,832	1,624	1,397	1,473	2,432	2,346	1,636
15								386	636	101			545
Total	6,400	6,639	6,820	7,147	7,453	7,539	7,343	7,627	7,562	8,148	9,098	9,486	10,089

*Annual earnings courtesy of The United States Trotting Association

Season Earnings for Trotters

Age	1985	1986	1987	1988	1989	1990	1991	1992	1993	1994	1995	1996	1997
2	$9,706	9,303	9,215	9,711	9,241	10,257	9,835	10,116	10,058	10,421	11,155	11,698	11,977
3	10,318	10,602	10,213	10,028	10,675	10,394	10,963	10,920	10,742	11,373	12,584	12,631	13,409
4	6,086	6,150	5,986	7,222	6,308	5,498	5,432	6,741	7,079	7,202	8,604	8,157	9,232
5	7,194	6,729	7,374	7,359	8,356	7,781	7,061	7,378	7,871	7,752	9,482	10,005	10,230
6	6,195	6,547	7,789	6,901	7,191	8,582	7,303	8,774	7,869	8,486	9,487	10,754	11,879
7	6,911	5,605	6,201	6,883	7,531	7,993	8,144	8,340	8,474	8,119	9,411	9,563	10,059
8	5,959	5,923	4,711	8,304	5,295	6,602	6,598	7,354	6,480	5,904	8,286	8,886	9,355
9	4,099	5,115	5,498	4,374	4,719	5,011	5,427	6,953	5,937	5,422	6,085	6,589	9,407
10	4,272	4,054	4,060	4,972	3,839	3,875	3,597	4,666	6,554	5,814	6,178	4,844	6,808
11	2,811	4,415	3,296	3,536	3,857	3,212	3,665	2,595	4,014	5,851	5,921	4,188	5,602
12	2,648	3,172	2,431	3,555	3,451	3,609	2,089	2,409	2,895	3,710	5,665	5,228	5,222
13	2,617	2,311	2,376	2,577	1,463	2,904	2,815	1,802	2,041	2,976	3,910	5,724	4,851
14	3,076	2,986	1,918	1,765	2,289	1,665	2,769	2,245	1,255	1,802	1,261	2,981	9,768
15											128		
Total	7,602	7,639	7,731	8,127	8,068	8,252	8,118	8,677	8,656	8,894	10,094	10,333	11,100

*Annual earnings courtesy of The United States Trotting Association

Index

A Gleam, 56, 61
Ace Card, 55
Aegina, 56
All Blue, 55
Alopatia, 50
American Glory, 55
Ancestor, 54-55
Anthemion, 55
Apogee, 55
Athenia, 56
Australian, 24
Bahram, 55-56, 68
Bala Ormont, 55
Balladier, 56
Battle Morn, 55
Bazaar, 55
Be Faithful, 55
Be Fearless, 55
Be Fleet, 55
Beard, Clarkson, 43
Beau Dandy, 56
Bee Mac, 55
Bella Figura, 56
Ben Brush, 17, 24, 33
Bend Or, 24-25, 29, 33, 71
Bernborough, 56
Bernwood, 56
Best Seller, 55
Better Self, 55, 61
Big Hurry, 55
Big If, 56
Bimelech, 55
Birdcatcher, 24
Black Tarquin, 57, 61
Black Toney, 17

Black Wave, 55
Blandford, 46
Blenheim II, 55-56, 68-69
Bloodroot, 55
Blue Delight, 55
Blue Larkspur, 55-56, 73
Bonnie Scotland, 24
Bonus, 25
Boswell, 56
Boswell Lady, 56
Brazado, 55
Bric A Bac, 55
Bridal Flower, 55, 61
Broad Ripple, 55
Bryan G., 55
Bubbley, 55
Bull Dog, 55-56, 68
Bull Lea, 46, 55-57, 68-69, 73
Bull Page, 56
Bully Boy, 55
Burgoo King, 55
Campbell, J.B., 43
Capot, 56, 61
Capot, 56, 61
Catalysis, 55
Chains, 55
Challedon, 55
Challenger II, 55
Challtack, 52
Chance Play, 56
Charnot, 50
Ciencia, 55
Citation, 45
Clark Chief, 20
Cocopet, 55

93

Columbiana, 55
Cork Elm, 20
Cosmic Missile, 56
Count Fleet, 46, 55-56, 68-69
Counterpoint, 56, 61
Creole Maid, 55
Cromwell, James W., 20
Curandero, 55
Cyllene, 24
Dark Discovery, 55
De Luxe, 56
Dinner Date, 55
Diomed, 24
Domino, 24-25, 33, 71
Donita M., 55
Donitas First, 55
Duchess Peg, 56
Durazna, 56
Easy Whirl, 56
Eclipse, 24, 27, 73
Eight Thirty, 56
Equipoise, 46
Esposa, 55
Esteem, 55
Eternal Reward, 55
Faberose, 55
Fair Play, 17, 24, 33
Fair Weather, 55
Far Star, 55
Farmerette, 55
Faultless, 57
Ficklebush, 55
Firethorn, 55
Fleeting Star, 55
Flood Town, 55
Floradora, 55
Forever Yours, 55

Free America, 55
Gallant Duke, 56
Gallant Fox, 21-22, 25
Galopin, 24, 29, 33
Glencoe, 24
Godolphin Arabian, 24
Good Morning, 55
Gordon, Alex B., 75
Greek Ship, 45
Hampton, 24, 33
Handcuff, 55
Hank H., 52
Hanover, 24, 28-29, 33
Hard Tack, 55-56
Harrison Chief, 20
Hash, 56
He Did, 26, 29, 56
Heliopolis, 48, 56
Hermit, 24, 33
Herod, 24, 27, 73
High Trend, 56
Highflyer, 24
Hindoo, 24
Holeman, Del, 18
Hull Down, 55
Hurry On, 37
Hyperion, 46, 71-72
Hypnotist II, 56
Imperatrice, 55
Iseult, 55
Isonomy, 24-25, 29, 33
Jabot, 56
Jack High, 56
Jacola, 56
Jamestown, 55
Jennie Lee, 56
Jet Pilot, 55, 57, 61
Jet Pilot, 55, 57, 61

94

Jet's Date, 57
Johnstown, 55, 68
Kilroe, F.E., 43
King Cole, 56
Kit Carson, 56
Leamington, 29
Lee Axworthy, 32
Lexington, 24
Light Lady, 56
Little Risk, 56
Lowe, Bruce, 35, 72-73,
    78, 81
Lush, Jay L., 7-9, 35
Lute Boyd, 20
Mac Bea, 55
Mahmoud, 48, 55-56, 68
Mahmoudess, 55
Mahubah, 24
Man o'War, 20, 24, 37,
    45, 71
Manatella, 56
Mar-Kell, 56
Marguerite, 21-22, 24
Mark-Ye-Well, 54, 56, 61,
    69
Mata Hari, 56
Matchem, 27
Melbourne, 24
Menow, 56
Menu, 55
Merry Lassie, 55
Miss Bunting, 56
Miss Dogwood, 56
Miss Dolphin, 56
Miss Ferdinand, 56
Miss Merriment, 56
Miss Mommy, 55
Misty Isle, 56

Mohammedan, 56
Motto, 56
Mr. Trouble, 56
Mrs. Ames, 55-56
Myrtlewood, 56
Nasca, 56
Natchez, 55
Navigating, 55
Navy Page, 54, 56
Nellie Flag, 56
Nellie L., 56
Newminster, 24
Next Move, 56, 61
Now What, 56
Occupation, 56, 61
Occupy, 56
Ocean Wave, 55
Olympia, 56, 61
Omaha, 57
One Count, 54-55, 61, 69
Our Boots, 56
Our Page, 56
Page Boots, 56
Painted Veil, 56
Partner, 24
Petrify, 56
Phalanx, 56, 61
Pharamond II, 36-37, 56
Pictor, 56
Pictus, 56
Pilate, 56
Piping Rock, 55
Piquet, 56
Pochahontas, 24
Pompey, 55
Post Card, 55
Prevaricator, 57
Prophets Thumb, 55

Proud One, 56
Put Out, 55
Real Delight, 54-55, 61, 69
Reaping Reward, 55
Rhodes Scholar, 57
Riot, 56
Rippey, 55, 61
Risk A Whirl, 56
Roman, 55-56
Rose Beam, 56
Rosemont, 55
Roseretter, 56
Rosetown, 56
Sabaean, 55
Safe Arrival, 56
Salaminia, 56
Salmagundi, 56
Sarazen, 29
Scattered, 55
Sea Snack, 56
Sequence, 56
Service Pilot, 56
Sharp, F. Mainwaring, 33
Shut Out, 55
Sickle, 37, 55
Sir Archy, 24
Sir Damion, 56
Sir Gallahad III, 17, 21-22, 24, 67-68, 71
Some Chance, 56-57
Some Pomp, 56
Sonic, 56
Split Second, 56
Sport Page, 56
Spy Song, 56, 61
Squared Away, 55
St. Germans, 25

St. Simon, 24-25, 28-29, 33, 46, 71
Star Pilot, 55
Star Reward, 55
Steadfast, 55
Stimulus, 55
Stockwell, 24
Stone Age, 56, 74
Stunts, 56
Sweep, 17
Sweep All, 67-68
Sysonby, 32
Tailspin, 56
Tangled, 56
Teddy, 71
The Admiral, 55
The Porter, 45
Too Timely, 56
Toro Nancy, 56
Touchstone, 24
Twenty Grand, 25
Twilight Tear, 56
Two And Twenty, 56
Two Bob, 57
Two Lea, 57, 61
Twosy, 57
Unerring, 57
Vagrancy, 57
Voltaire, 24
Vuillier, 35, 72-73
Vulcania, 57
War Admiral, 55-56, 68
War Date, 57
Whirlaway, 55-56, 68
White Lies, 57
Wise Counsellor, 29
Yildiz, 55